Disney Princess

This annual belongs to

georgie

Watt

EGMONT

We bring stories to life

First published in Great Britain 2013 by Egmont UK Limited
The Yellow Building, 1 Nicholas Road, London W11 4AN

Edited by Jane Riordan and Jude Exley. Designed by Catherine Ellis.

© 2013 Disney Enterprises, Inc./ Pixar. All rights reserved.
The movie The Princess and the Frog © 2009 Disney, story inspired in part
by the book The Frog Princess by E.D. Baker © 2002, published by Bloomsbury Publishing, Inc.

ISBN 978 1 4052 6645 1
54719/1
Printed in Italy

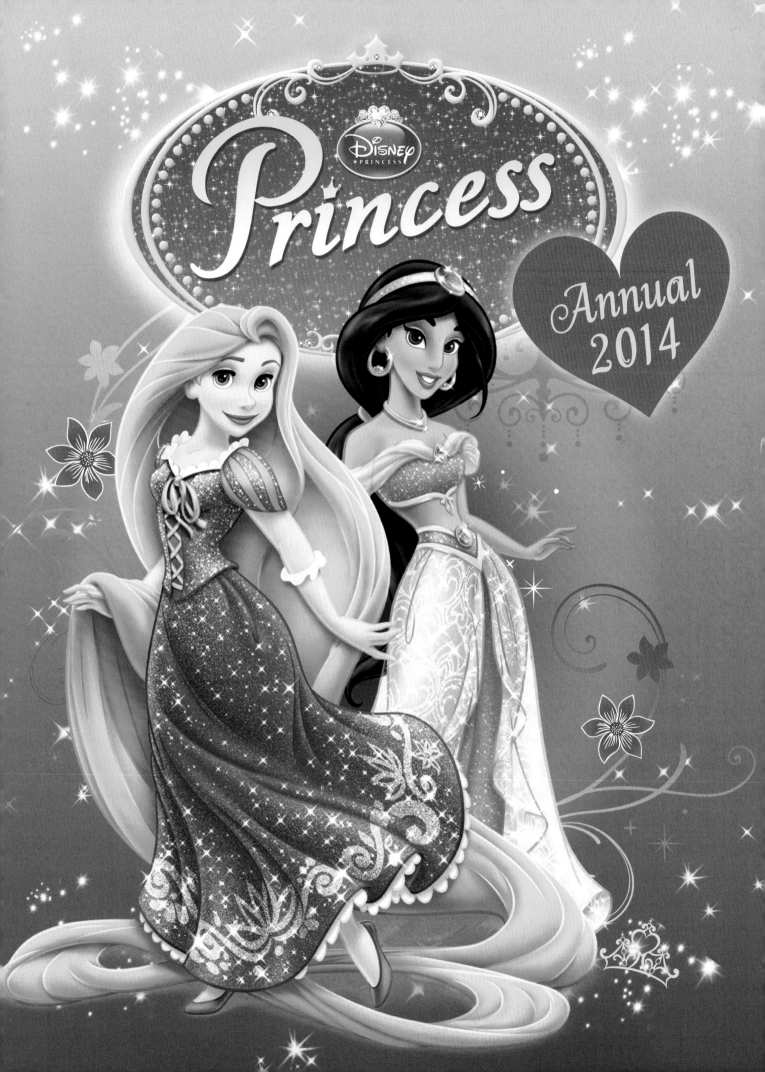

Rapunzel

Rapunzel

Tiana & Jasmine

Tiana   Jasmine

Belle

Belle

Aurora

Aurora

A chance to win £150 of book tokens!

See page 67 for details.

NATIONAL BOOK tokens

Meet the Princesses

Rapunzel
Rapunzel loves to go on adventures with her friends!

Jasmine
Jasmine teaches her friends to be independent and strong.

Snow White
Trusting and gentle, Snow White is a truly loyal friend.

Tiana
Tiana cooks delicious treats for her friends!

Ariel
Ariel shares her deepest secrets with her underwater friends.

Friends Forever!

Merida

Passionate and fiery, Merida is a strong, outgoing friend.

Belle

Belle's best friend makes dazzling dresses for her!

Cinderella

Cinderella loves organising parties for her friends!

Aurora

Aurora's best friends are the animals in the forest.

Make friends with ...

Ariel

Everything you need to know about your new friend:

Ariel is King Triton's youngest daughter.

She is brave enough to risk everything to make her dreams come true.

She lives in a beautiful underwater world with her sisters.

Ariel longs to be part of the human world, especially when she meets handsome Prince Eric.

She tells all her secrets to her fishy friend, Flounder.

Ariel loves looking at the beautiful fashions in the human world. She longs to wear dresses like them.

Draw a picture of yourself wearing your favourite outfit so that Ariel knows all about your style.

Now that you are friends, Ariel has a secret just for you ...

The impossible can become possible if you really want it enough.

Summer Trends

1 One summer's day, Ariel saw a princess walking along the seafront. She was wearing a pretty gown. "She looks so beautiful," said Ariel.

2 "You're not the only one who thinks so," giggled Flounder. All the other girls were admiring her dress, too.

3 "I want a dress like hers," cried Ariel. She swam down to a wreck and found an old sail. She also collected pieces of coral.

4 Ariel soon made a dress just like the princess's. "You look wonderful," Ariel's sisters cried.

5 When Ariel swam to the surface again, every girl was wearing a dress just like the princess's.

6 At that very moment, the princess appeared. She was wearing a new dress that was even prettier than the last one.

7 "Wow," gasped Ariel. She swam down to search for things she could use to copy the princess's latest look.

8 However this time, Ariel couldn't find anything at all to make a similar dress. "Oh well," she sighed.

9 Instead, Ariel decided to have some fun creating her own look. She made a dress from different shades of green seaweed.

10 She made some jewellery, too. "That outfit looks as good as the princess's dresses," said Flounder.

11 Just then, Flounder heard a noise. "Divers!" he cried, in panic.

12 They kept well hidden while the divers explored the ship. One of the divers saw Ariel's dress and spent a long time admiring it.

13 "There's no treasure here," whispered Flounder. "That all depends on what you call treasure," replied Ariel. Eventually, the divers swam away.

14 A few days later, Ariel swam up to look at the seafront. All the girls were wearing pink dresses, just like the princess's.

15 Suddenly, all the girls became excited when they saw the princess in a new outfit. It was just like the seaweed dress Ariel had designed.

16 "The princess must have been one of those divers!" gasped Ariel. "What a trendsetter you are, Ariel!" chuckled Flounder. "Soon, everyone will be wearing your dress on the seafront!"

The End

Fishy Friends Counting

Can you help Ariel find her way to the finish?
Have fun tracing over the numbers and
counting along the way.

Start

one turtle

1

seven purple and pink fish

eight pink sea-flowers

8

7

nine pink and blue fish

Can you find Sebastian?

9

Use the number line to help you.

1 2 3 4 5 6

two kissing fish

2

three singing fish

3

four seahorses

4

five starfish

5

six orange fish

6

ten bubbles

10

Draw yourself here.

7 8 9 10

Finish

17

Make Friends with ...

Cinderella

Everything you need to know about your new friend:

She has a cruel stepmother called Lady Tremaine.

Her two jealous stepsisters are called Anastasia and Drizella.

Her fairy godmother made all her wishes come true.

Cinderella has a great sense of humour and you'll often hear her laughing.

She loves to dance, especially with the handsome Prince Charming!

Her best friends are the cheeky mice, Gus and Jaq.

Before Cinderella was a Princess she had to work
hard at home doing lots of chores.
Tell Cinderella all about what you do at home to help.

At home I help out by:

....

My least favourite job is:

....

Now that you are friends, Cinderella has a secret
just for you ...

There has only been one day happier than the
night of the Royal Ball — my wedding day!

The Fairy Tree

1 Since living at the palace, Cinderella had spent many happy hours swinging on the old oak tree in the garden. She felt the tree was somehow special.

2 All the creatures that lived in the old oak also felt the happy energy.

3 But early one morning, Cinderella was woken by a thunderous crash in the garden. The old oak tree had finally toppled over.

4 The terrified creatures that lived in the tree fled away from the garden in panic. "This is terrible," cried Cinderella, as the garden became empty and silent.

5 Just then, Cinderella heard the faintest sound of sobbing coming from the tree. To her amazement, a hollow opened in the trunk.

6 Inside the hollow, was a glowing fairy. "I knew this tree was special," gasped Cinderella. "Oh, Cinderella, this oak was more special than you can imagine," cried the fairy.

7 "Every forest, wood, park and garden starts with a fairy tree," explained the fairy. "Its happiness spreads out in all directions. But without fairy trees, the land all around will become sad."

8 "What will happen to you?" worried Cinderella. "As it fades, my light will fade, too," whispered the fairy.

9 "I've had so many wonderful times here," sighed Cinderella, as she remembered a romantic picnic she once had with the Prince.

11 Cinderella's memories suddenly made the fairy glow a little brighter. "The happiness that poured out of the tree can be poured back in," gasped Cinderella.

12 The garden creatures poured their happy memories into the tree too. The dazzling fairy danced with delight, as new leaves began to sprout on the old oak. "Thank you, Cinderella," beamed the Fairy.

The End

Feathered Friends

Use your prettiest colours to finish this picture of Cinderella and her bird friends.

Which pair of birds do not appear in the picture?

a

b

Answer on page 65.

Make a Bird Feeder

This birdfeeder will give the birds a tasty treat!
Ask an adult to help you with each step.

You will need:
Empty milk carton
Masking tape
Paint
Paintbrush
Safety scissors
Unsharpened pencil
Birdseed
String

1 Tape the top shut on the milk carton. Paint it your favourite colour and let it dry.

2 Cut a hole on one side, big enough for a bird.

3 Ask an adult to poke a pencil through the carton, about 2cm below the hole.

4 Decorate the carton however you'd like. Use bright colours that birds can spot!

6 Poke a hole through the carton top to tie on some string. Then ask an adult to hang your birdfeeder from a tree branch, out of reach of children and cats. The birds will love their yummy snack!

5 Put some birdseed in the hole.

Make Friends with ...

Merida

Everything you need to know about your new friend:

She is an accomplished archer and swordfighter.

Merida loves to race across the Scottish Highlands with her faithful horse, Angus.

She has three mischievous brothers called Harris, Hubert and Hamish.

Merida's hair is as fiery as her temper.

Merida shows true bravery when she sets out to undo a beastly curse.

Merida's triplet brothers keep her very busy indeed.
Tell Merida all about your family.

I have ☐ brother(s) called ....

I have ☐ sister(s) called ....

The naughtiest thing my brother or sister has ever done is:

....

Now that you are friends, Merida has a secret
just for you ...

I'd do anything for the triplets, even though they sometimes make me cross!

Cute Cub Friends

It's teatime! Help the cubs earn their treats by completing these puzzles.

Trace the paths below and count the number of bounces to see which bear will get to eat first. The bear with the most bounces wins!

a

b

c

The cubs are after a sweet treat. Only two of these buns are exactly the same – can you spot them?

a

b

c

d

e

f

g

h

Answers on page 65.

Make Your Own Poster

Disney · PIXAR

BRAVE

This Merida poster was coloured by:

....

Troublesome Triplets

Merida's naughty brothers are hiding in the forest.
Can you help her find them, by following the correct path?

a

m

w

n

i

h

o

Start

t

s

h

Finish

Find out who Merida will reach first, by writing the letters you pass in the spaces below.

_____ _____ _____ _____ _____ _____ _____

Write your answer here.

Answer on page 65.

Make Friends with ...

Snow White

Everything you need to know about your new friend:

Snow White is as kind as she is pretty.

She loves taking good care of her friends, the seven dwarfs.

Snow White is really a Princess, but her wicked stepmother treats her like a servant.

She is so gentle that wild animals trust her and are happy to perch on her shoulders.

Snow White is always ready to cheer up anyone who is having a difficult day.

Snow White loves animals.
Tell her all about you and animals:

My favourite animal is:

....

If I could have any pet in the world, I would have a:

....

I would call my pet:

....

Now that you are friends, Snow White has a secret just for you ...

The magic mirror tells me that we're going to be the very best of friends!

Pony Playmate

Add some bright colours to this lovely picture of Snow White and her horse.

Add some colour to the butterfly, rabbit and chipmunk, too.

Forest Friends

Snow White is playing in the forest with her animal friends.
Can you spot six differences in picture b?
Colour a paw print as you find each one.

a

b

Love Birds

Use the picture key to help you read this Snow White story!

| Prince | bird | rose petals | berries |

It was a sunny day and Snow White

was walking through the forest, when

she noticed something at the side of

the path. It was a little with a

damaged wing. "Oh dear," said Snow

White, as she picked up the injured bird.

"Don't worry, I'll soon make you better."

Snow White carried the to the

dwarfs' cottage. There she made her

comfortable and fed her fresh

 and seeds.

After a few days, the was

better and Snow White took her into

the forest to set her free.

When Snow White got back to the

cottage, however, the was

sitting outside the door waiting for her.

"I think you need a little help to get used to life back in the forest," said Snow White. So she filled a basket with  .

"This will make the perfect nest for you," said Snow White, as she fixed the nest into a tree. The snuggled into its new home. So Snow White was surprised to find the at the cottage window, later that afternoon. "Oh, dear!" said Snow White. "I wonder what's wrong?"

Snow White gave the some  and then walked back to her nest. The followed, but later on, she returned to the cottage.

Snow White was not sure how to help the , so she took her to the wishing well. "I wish I could make you happy," said Snow White.

As she said this, a boy flew down and sat next to the . The pair snuggled up together. Just then, the arrived and Snow White explained what had happened.

"I think she needed to find her true love," said the Prince, "just like I needed to find mine!"

The End

Make Friends with ...

Rapunzel

Everything you need to know about your new friend:

Rapunzel has the most extraordinary long, blonde hair – it's all thanks to a magical flower.

Every year on her birthday, Rapunzel's parents, the King and the Queen, send up lanterns into the night sky.

Rapunzel is very artistic and loves making crafts.

Her best friend is the cheeky chameleon, Pascal.

The love of Rapunzel's life is a young man called Flynn Rider.

Rapunzel has an adventurous spirit.
Draw a picture of you and Rapunzel having an adventure together.

Now that you are friends, Rapunzel has a secret just for you ...

Listen to your heart.
It will tell you what to do.

Chameleon Companion

Can you draw lines to put these pictures of Rapunzel's friend Pascal into pairs? Which picture is not part of a pair?

a

b

c

d

e

f

g

_____ is not part of a pair.

Answer on page 65.

Friends for Life

Can you work out which of these pictures of Rapunzel and Pascal are exactly the same, then colour in the picture?

a

b

c

Follow

d

and
are exactly
the same.

Answer on page 65.

Garden Friends

Add some friendly colours to this picture of Belle and the Enchanted Objects.

Colour this butterfly when you spot Cogsworth.

Point to the blue butterfly.

Answers on page 6

Belle Maze

Which path leads Belle to her beautiful tiara?

Answer on page 65

Start

a

b

c

necklace

tiara

ring

51

Friendship Quiz

Can you answer these questions about
Belle's friends by placing a tick in the correct hearts?

1 Which of these
is Chip's mother,
Mrs Potts?

a

b

2 Which Enchanted
Object is a candlestick?

a

b

Belle is my
best friend.
Who is yours?

friends

Trace over the word above.

3 Which Enchanted Object cleans the castle?

a

b

4 Which Enchanted Object wakes Belle up in the morning?

a

b

Can you spot Footstool?

Trace butterfli some to

Use these word

rose

Answers on page 66.

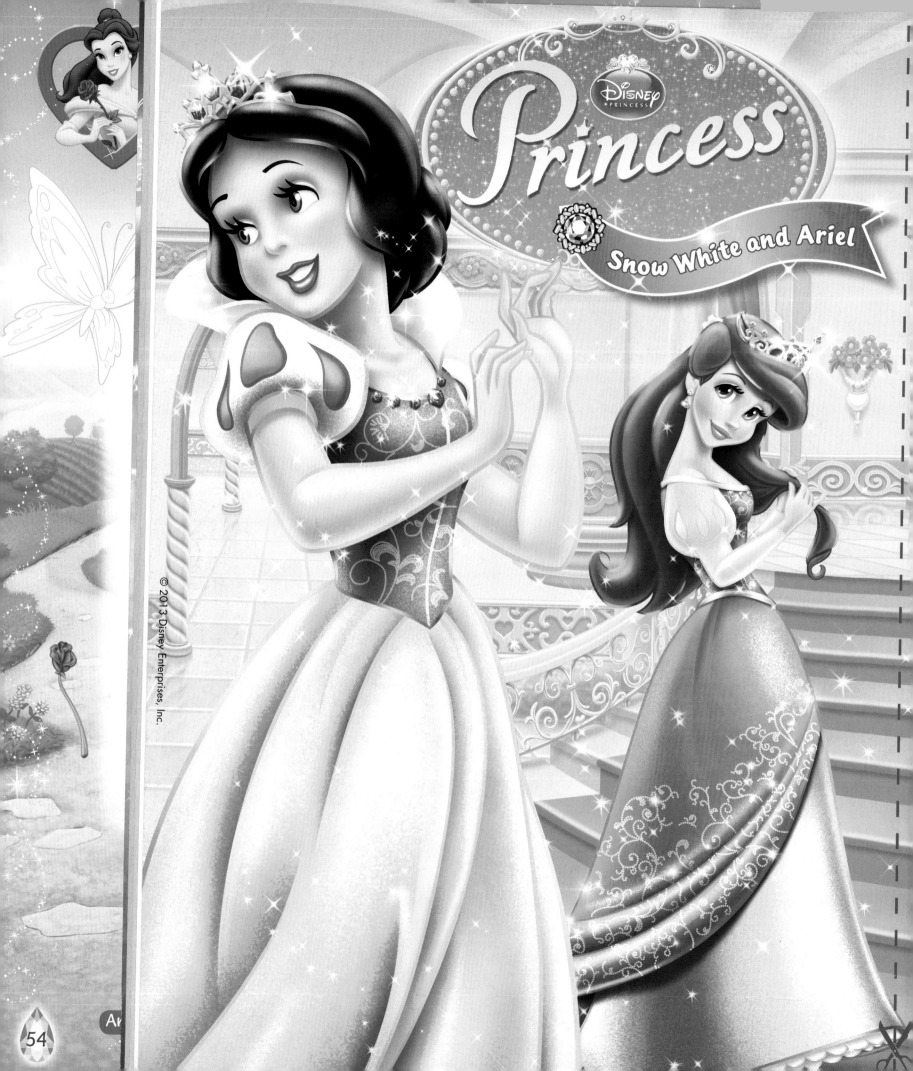

Disney PRINCESS

Princess

Snow White and Ariel

Answers

Page 24 Feathered Friends

Birds b do not appear in the picture.

Page 28 Cute Cub Friends

1. a-6 bounces, b-5 bounces, c-7 bounces.
Bear cub c wins.
2. Buns b and f are the same.

Page 31 Troublesome Triplets

She finds Hamish first.

Page 35 Forest Friends

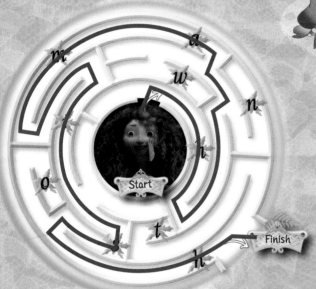

Page 40 Chameleon Companion

The pairs are: a and g, b and e, c and f.
Chameleon d is not part of a pair.

Page 41 Friends for Life

b and d are exactly the same.

Page 47 Animal Magic

Page 50 Garden Friends

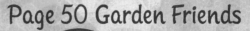

Page 51 Belle Maze

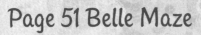

Start

a b c

Answer on page 65

necklace   tiara   ring

Pages 52-53 Friendship Quiz

1-b, 2-a, 3-a, 4-b.
Footstool is hiding behind Belle.

Pages 54-55 Surprise Story

Cogsworth is behind the bench.

Reader Survey

We'd love to know what you think about your Disney Princess Annual.

One lucky reader will win £150 of book tokens! Five runners-up will receive a £25 book token each.

NATIONAL BOOK tokens

Ask a grown-up to help you fill in this form and post it to the address at the end by 28th February 2014, or you can fill in the survey online at:

www.egmont.co.uk/disneyprincess-survey2014

1. Who bought this annual?

- ☐ Me
- ☐ Parent/guardian
- ☐ Grandparent
- ☐ Other (please specify)

_____

2. Why did they buy it?

- ☐ Christmas present
- ☐ Birthday present
- ☐ I'm a collector
- ☐ Other (please specify)

_____

3. What are your favourite parts of the annual?

	Really like	Like	Don't like
Stories	☐	☐	☐
Puzzles	☐	☐	☐
Colouring	☐	☐	☐
Make Friends with...	☐	☐	☐
Posters	☐	☐	☐
Drawing	☐	☐	☐

4. Do you think the stories are too long, too short or about right?

- ☐ Too long
- ☐ Too short
- ☐ About right

5. Do you think the activities are too hard, too easy or about right?

- ☐ Too hard
- ☐ Too easy
- ☐ About right

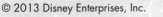

6. Who are your favourite Disney Princesses in this annual?

1. _____
2. _____
3. _____

7. Which other annuals have you bought this year?

1. _____
2. _____
3. _____

8. What is your favourite ...

1. ... app? _____
2. ... website? _____
3. ... console game? _____
4. ... magazine? _____
5. ... book? _____

9. What are your favourite TV programmes?

1. _____
2. _____
3. _____

10. Have you bought a Disney Annual before? If so, which ones?

1. _____
2. _____
3. _____

11. Would you like to get another Disney Annual again next year?

☐ Yes   ☐ No

Why? _____
_____

Thank you!
(Please ask your parent/guardian to complete)

Child's name: _____ Age: _____ Boy/Girl

Parent/guardian name: _____

Parent/guardian signature: _____

Parent/guardian email address: _____

Daytime telephone number: _____

☐ Please send me the Egmont Monthly Catch-Up Newsletter.

Please cut out this form and post to: Disney Princess Annual Reader Survey, Egmont UK Limited, The Yellow Building, 1 Nicholas Road, London, W11 4AN

Good luck!

© 2013 Disney